THE MAHABHARATA
CHILDREN'S ILLUSTRATED CLASSICS

BIRTH of the ROYAL PRINCES

Retold by **CHARU AGARWAL DHANDIA**
Art **KAVITA SINGH KALE**   *Design* **RACHITA RAKYAN**

RUPA

Published by
Rupa Publications India Pvt. Ltd 2020
7/16, Ansari Road, Daryaganj
New Delhi 110002

Sales centres:
Allahabad Bengaluru Chennai
Hyderabad Jaipur Kathmandu
Kolkata Mumbai

Edition copyright © Rupa Publications Pvt. Ltd 2020

All rights reserved.
No part of this publication may be reproduced, transmitted,
or stored in a retrieval system, in any form or by any means, electronic, mechanical, photocopying,
recording or otherwise,
without the prior permission of the publisher.

ISBN: 978-81-291-4970-1

First impression 2020

10 9 8 7 6 5 4 3 2 1

The moral right of the author has been asserted.

Printed at Nutech Print Services - India

This book is sold subject to the condition that it shall not, by way of trade or otherwise, be lent, resold, hired out, or otherwise circulated, without the publisher's prior consent, in any form of binding or cover other than that in which it is published.

Charu Agarwal Dhandia weaves together her two biggest passions—studying Indian classical literature and creative storytelling. She is an economist by training and works in the social development space.

Kavita Singh Kale's background as an artist and a designer enables her to draw a thin line between design following functionality and pure self-expression. This has helped her evolve as a transmedia artist. Her work includes art installations, children's books, comics, paintings and videos.

Rachita Rakyan combines over 15 years of expertise in graphic design and art direction with deep understanding of functionality and aesthetics across print, publishing, branding and digital media.

CONTENTS

KURU DYNASTY	IV–V
KEY CHARACTERS	VI–VII
PANDAVAS AND KAURAVAS	1
BIRTH OF PANDU'S SONS	7
BIRTH OF KARNA	15
DURYODHANA'S EVIL PLANS	25
DRUPADA AND DRONACHARYA	37
DRONACHARYA IN HASTINAPUR	47

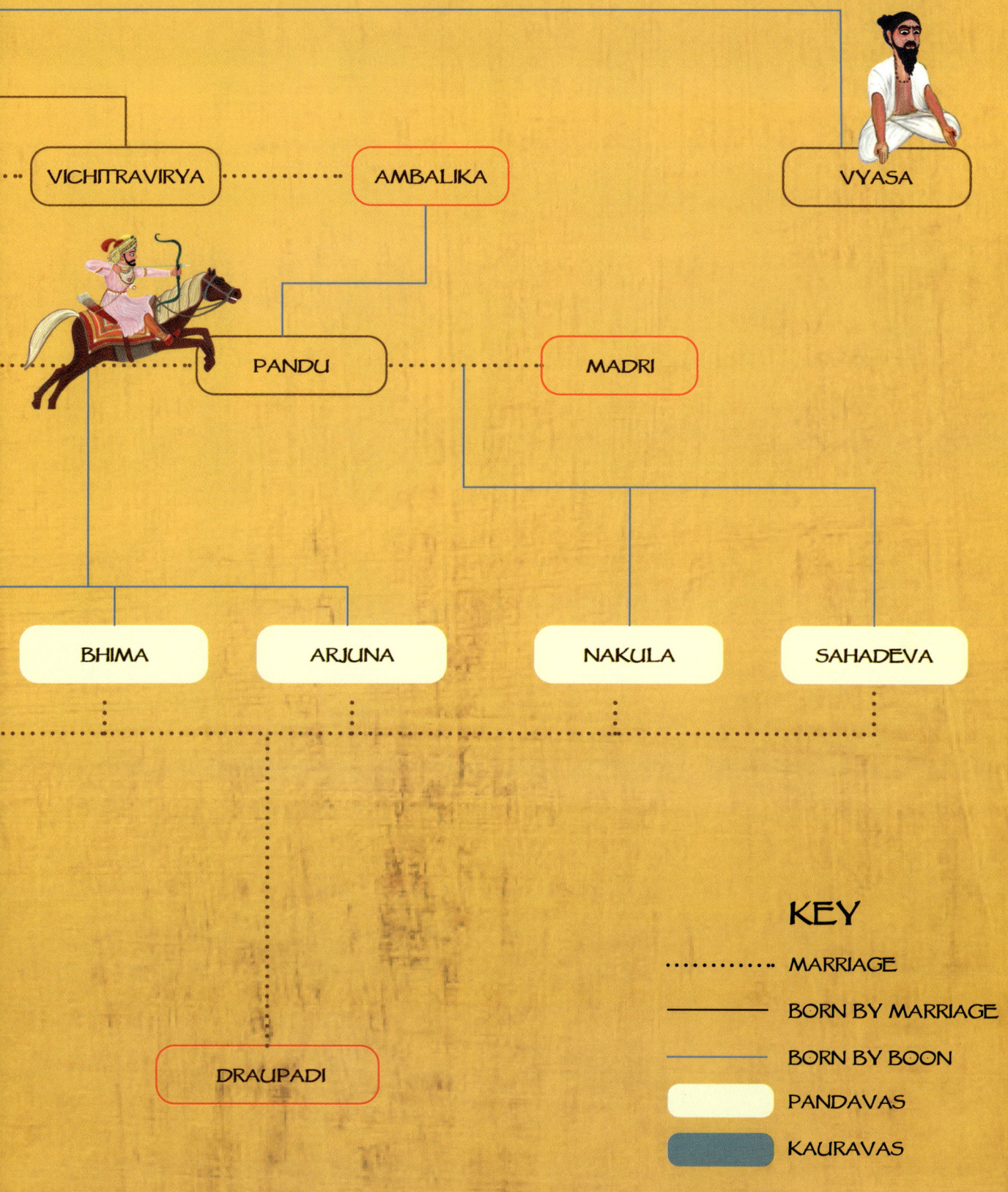

KEY CHARACTERS

PANDU

Pandu the brave ruler of Hastinapur, who was widely known for his strength and wisdom. He married princesses Kunti and Madri and became father to the five Pandavas with the help of Kunti's magical chant given to her by sage Durvasa.

KUNTI

Kunti, the daughter of King Kuntibhoja, was blessed by sage Durvasa for taking care of him. He gave her a magic chant that she could use to make any god appear and give her a son. Using this chant when she was very young, she got Karna, a son from the sun god, Surya. Later five Pandava brothers were born with the help of the chant.

KARNA

Karna was born to young Kunti by the boon of Lord Surya. He was raised by a charioteer Adhiratha and his wife Radha. Later, he became a supremely skilled archer known for his loyalty and friendship with Duryodhana.

DURYODHANA

Duryodhana was the eldest brother amongst the Kauravas and born to princess Gandhari as a blessing from sage Vyasa. He was very jealous of the Pandavas.

VYASA

The immortal sage who composed the Mahabharata. Vyasa was born to Satyavati. Later, he gave boons for the birth of Dhrithrashtra, Pandu and the hundred Kaurava brothers.

DRONACHARYA

Dronacharya was guru to the Pandava and the Kaurava princes while they were growing up in Hastinapur. Although Dronacharya loved all the princes, he was most fond of Arjuna. Dronacharya married Kripi and was the father of Ashwatthama.

PANDAVAS AND KAURAVAS

King Pandu was the ruler of Hastinapur. He was a brave and fearless warrior. During his rule, the Kuru dynasty spread far and wide. Pandu had two queens, Kunti and Madri. One day, when Pandu was hunting in the forest, he spotted a beautiful deer behind some bushes. Pandu shot an arrow at the deer. To Pandu's shock, the deer suddenly turned into a sage!

As the sage fell down dying, he cursed Pandu, 'Oh king, since you have hurt me for no reason, you must be punished! You will remain childless all your life.'

Pandu felt very sad and regretted killing an innocent being. He decided to leave Hastinapur and went to live in the forest with his wives.

A few months passed in the forest but Pandu remained unhappy. Kunti loved Pandu and was unable to see his grief. She said, 'King, I have a secret that I have kept from you for years. I want to tell you today as it might end our misery.'
And so Kunti began narrating the story of Durvasa's boon to Pandu.

Many years ago, the mighty sage Durvasa came to meet Kunti's father Kuntibhoja. Kuntibhoja called Kunti and said, "Sage Durvasa is our guest. You must take great care of him." Kunti obeyed her father and took care of Durvasa for an entire year. Durvasa was very impressed by Kunti's devotion. He said, "Kunti, I want to give you a boon." He shut his eyes and muttered a prayer.

He gave her a magical chant and said, "When you repeat this and think of a God, you will be blessed with a child who has all the powers of that God. Be very careful Kunti, the chant can be used only five times!"

Saying this, Durvasa left.

BIRTH OF PANDU'S SONS

Pandu's face lit up with happiness! 'Oh Kunti, please use the magical chant to give birth to our children!' Pandu cried. Kunti agreed happily.

First, Kunti called upon Dharma, the God of Righteousness. He blessed her with their first son, Yudhishthira.

Next, she called upon Pavan, the Wind God and was blessed with their second son, Bhima.

Then she called upon Indra, the Rain God and was blessed with their third son, Arjuna.

Pandu said, 'Dear Kunti, I have one more request. Please give the chant to Madri as well. She is also childless and unhappy.'
Kunti was a kind person. She selflessly gave the chant to Madri.

Later in the night, Madri called upon the twin Gods Ashwins and was blessed with two sons, Nakula and Sahadeva. Pandu now had five sons—Yudhishthira, Bhima, Arjuna, Nakula and Sahadeva.
Together, Pandu's sons were called the Pandavas.

The news of the birth of the Pandavas reached Hastinapur. Pandu's elder brother Dhrithrashtra was blind. His queen was Gandhari, the princess of Gandhar. Gandhari loved her husband so much that she tied a piece of cloth on her eyes. She did not want to see what he could not!

When Gandhari heard of the Pandavas, she was very worried. She was scared that Yudhishthira would become the Kuru King since she did not have a son.

So, Gandhari called upon the great sage Vyasa and requested him to bless her with children.
Vyasa chanted a mantra and Gandhari gave birth to one hundred sons and a daughter, Dussala.
Together, they were called the Kauravas.

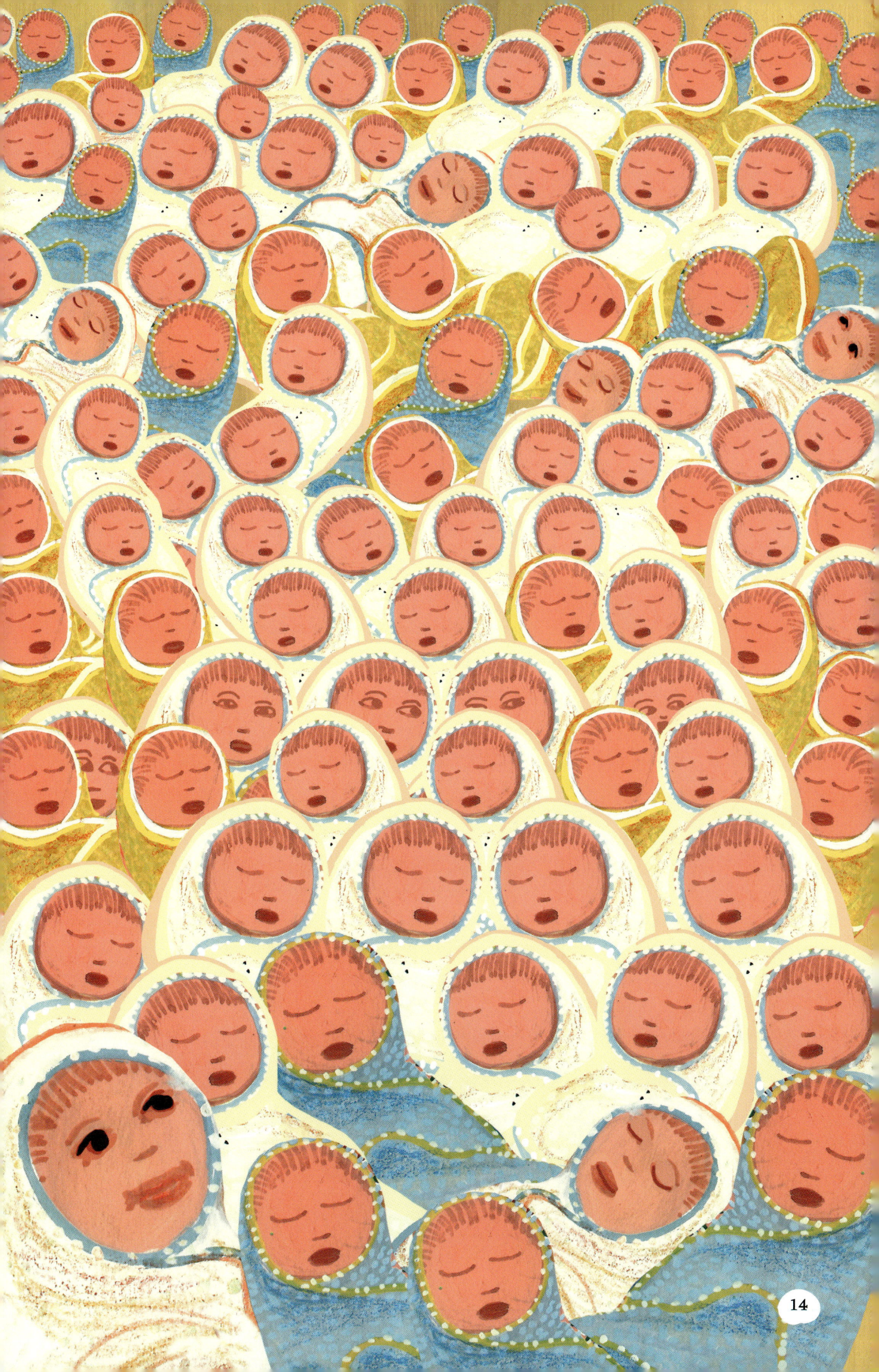

BIRTH OF KARNA

Long ago, when Kunti was young, she was curious to try out Durvasa's boon. So one day, she looked up at the bright sun and thinking of Surya, the Sun God, she spoke the magic words Durvasa had given her. Immediately Surya appeared in front of her.

Now Kunti was nervous! She folded her hands and said, "Lord, I used the chant out of curiosity. I have been careless. Forgive me."

Surya replied, "It is too late. The boon cannot be taken back. It holds me in its power. I will bless you with a son."

The next moment, Kunti had a beautiful baby boy in her lap. He wore golden earrings and golden armour on his chest. She named him Karna.

But Kunti was young and did not know what to do with the baby. She was helpless! She put Karna in a small basket and set it floating in river Ganga.

With tears in her eyes, she said, "Forgive me son, for leaving you alone. Hope you stay safe wherever you go."

The basket with Karna floated towards the bank. Adhiratha, a young charioteer, was passing by. He saw the basket floating down and became curious.

Adhiratha swam to the basket. He looked inside and saw little Karna smiling. Adhiratha had no children of his own. Adhiratha's face lit up with happiness and he thought, "I must take the baby home and keep him safe!"

Adhiratha picked up Karna and went home to his wife, Radha. He called out loudly, "Come quickly Radha, look what I have got!"

Radha came running. She was thrilled to see little Karna. She exclaimed, "God has heard our prayers. This baby is God's gift to us. We must raise him as our own son."

For years, Adhiratha and Radha raised Karna with great love and affection, like their own son. This is why Karna came to be known as *Sarathiputra*, the son of a charioteer.

Karna was a good child. He brought a lot of happiness into their home. He grew up to be a strong and handsome young man.

DURYODHANA'S EVIL PLANS

All this while, Pandu was living happily with his five sons and two wives in the forest. One day, Pandu passed away. Madri said to Kunti in sorrow, 'Sister, please take care of my two sons, Nakula and Sahadeva.'

Kunti brought all the five Pandava brothers to Hastinapur and began to live in Dhrithrashtra's palace.

All day, the five Pandavas would study and play with their cousins, the Kauravas. They lived together in the palace like one big family.

Duryodhana was the eldest son of Dhrithrashtra. After Pandu passed away, Duryodhana wanted to become the King of Hastinapur. But he was afraid that the Pandava princes would also want to rule Hastinapur.

Uncle Shakuni helped Duryodhana think of ways to defeat the Pandavas so that Duryodhana could become the next king.

Duryodhana said to Shakuni, 'Bhima is the strongest among the Pandavas. To weaken all of them, I plan to kill Bhima.'

One evening, Duryodhana invited the Pandavas for a picnic on the banks of river Ganga. He brought some poisoned *laddoos* with him.
'I must make Bhima eat these *laddoos*,' Duryodhana thought to himself.

After playing for some time, the brothers sat down to rest. Not knowing Duryodhana's plan, Bhima took a *laddoo* and ate it. Then he took another *laddoo* and ate it up too.

In a few minutes, Bhima started feeling uneasy. He fell on the ground unconscious. Duryodhana quickly pushed Bhima into the river.

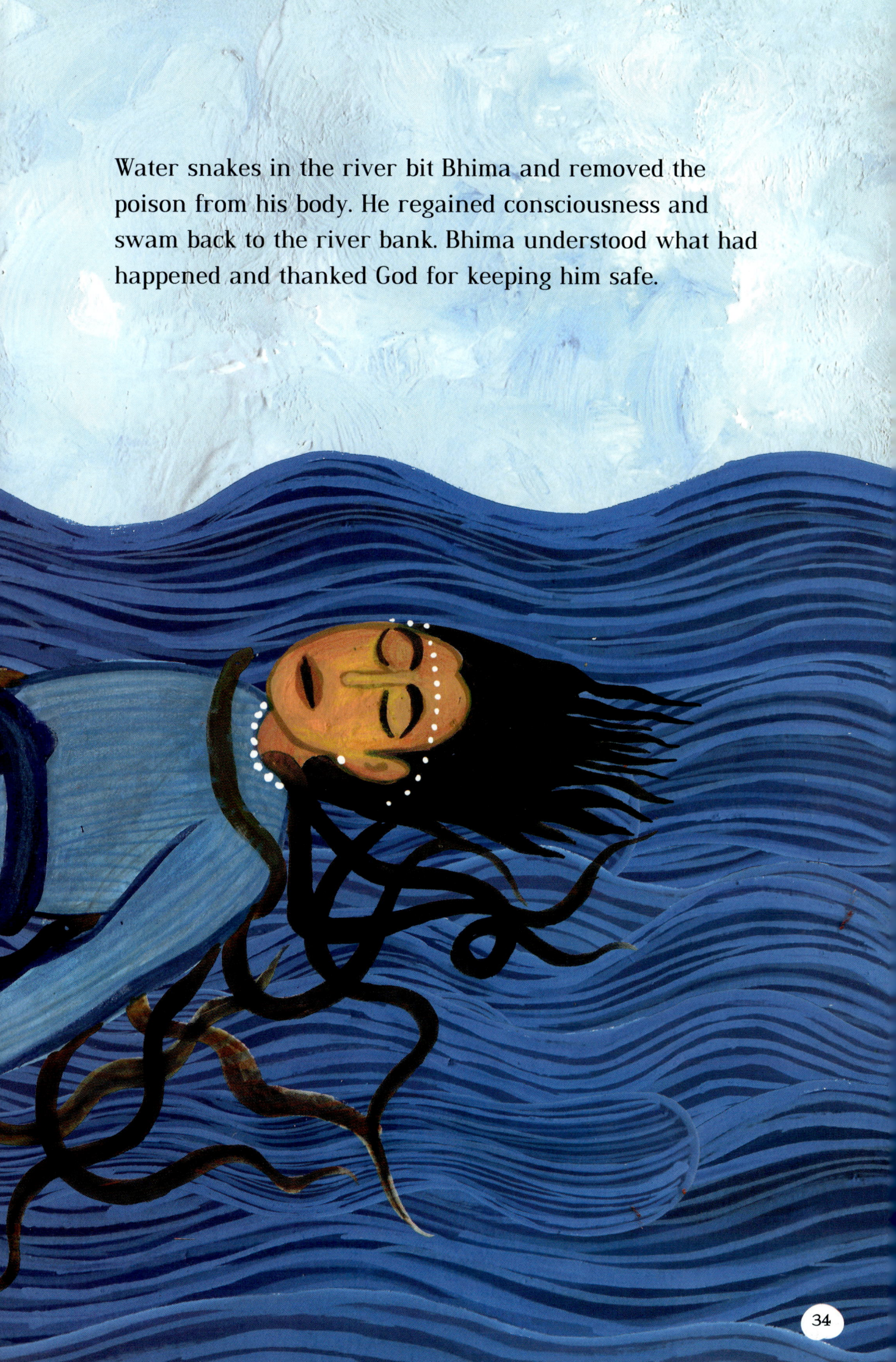

Water snakes in the river bit Bhima and removed the poison from his body. He regained consciousness and swam back to the river bank. Bhima understood what had happened and thanked God for keeping him safe.

Back in the palace, Bhima told his brothers what had happened. They understood that Duryodhana had poisoned the *laddoos* to kill them! From that day, the Pandavas became very careful of Duryodhana's actions.

DRUPADA AND DRONACHARYA

Kripacharya was the greatest teacher of martial arts in Hastinapur. Long ago, Kripacharya and his sister Kripi, who were orphans, had come to King Shantanu for shelter.

Shantanu was a kind-hearted king. He gave Kripacharya and Kripi a place to stay and took great care of them. In return, Kripacharya started teaching martial arts to the royal princes. Kripi got married to Dronacharya, the son of sage Bharadwaja.

Bhardwaja was a very famous archer. Under his guidance, his son Dronacharya became a master archer. Prince Drupada was also a student of Bhardwaja. Dronacharya and Drupada became close friends as they practised together under Bhardwaja.

One day, Drupada said to Dronacharya, 'My friend, I promise to share my kingdom with you when I become a king.'

Years went by and Drupada became the King of Panchala. Meanwhile, Dronacharya taught archery to his students and remained poor. He had a son called Ashwatthama whom he loved dearly.

One day, he saw some young boys making fun of Ashwatthama for being poor. Deeply hurt, he decided to go to his friend King Drupada to ask him for help.

Dronacharya reached Panchala and entered King Drupada's court. He said excitedly, 'Dear friend, I have come to meet you. I am so delighted to see you!'

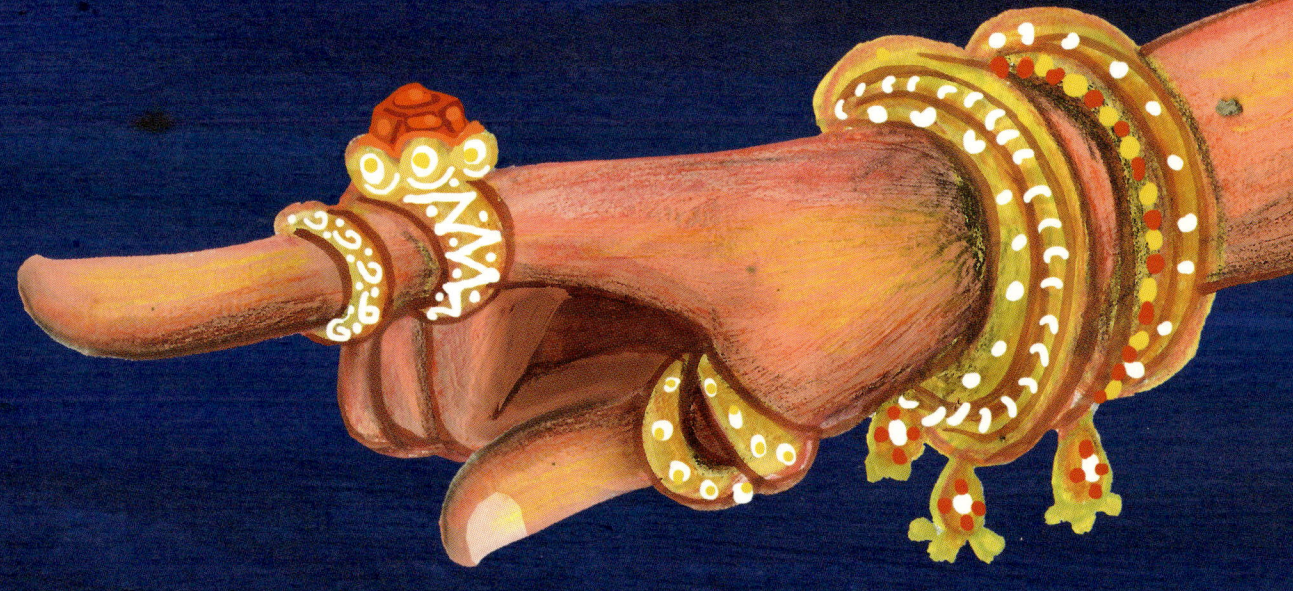

King Drupada retorted, 'You poor man! We were friends when we were young students. Now I am a king and you are a poor man. We cannot be friends anymore. Go away from here! Never come to see me again!'

Dronacharya realized that Drupada had forgotten his promise. His bitter words hurt Dronacharya. He left Drupada's palace in anger.

He thought to himself, 'One day, I will take revenge for this insult.'
Dronacharya went to Hastinapur and began living with Kripacharya.

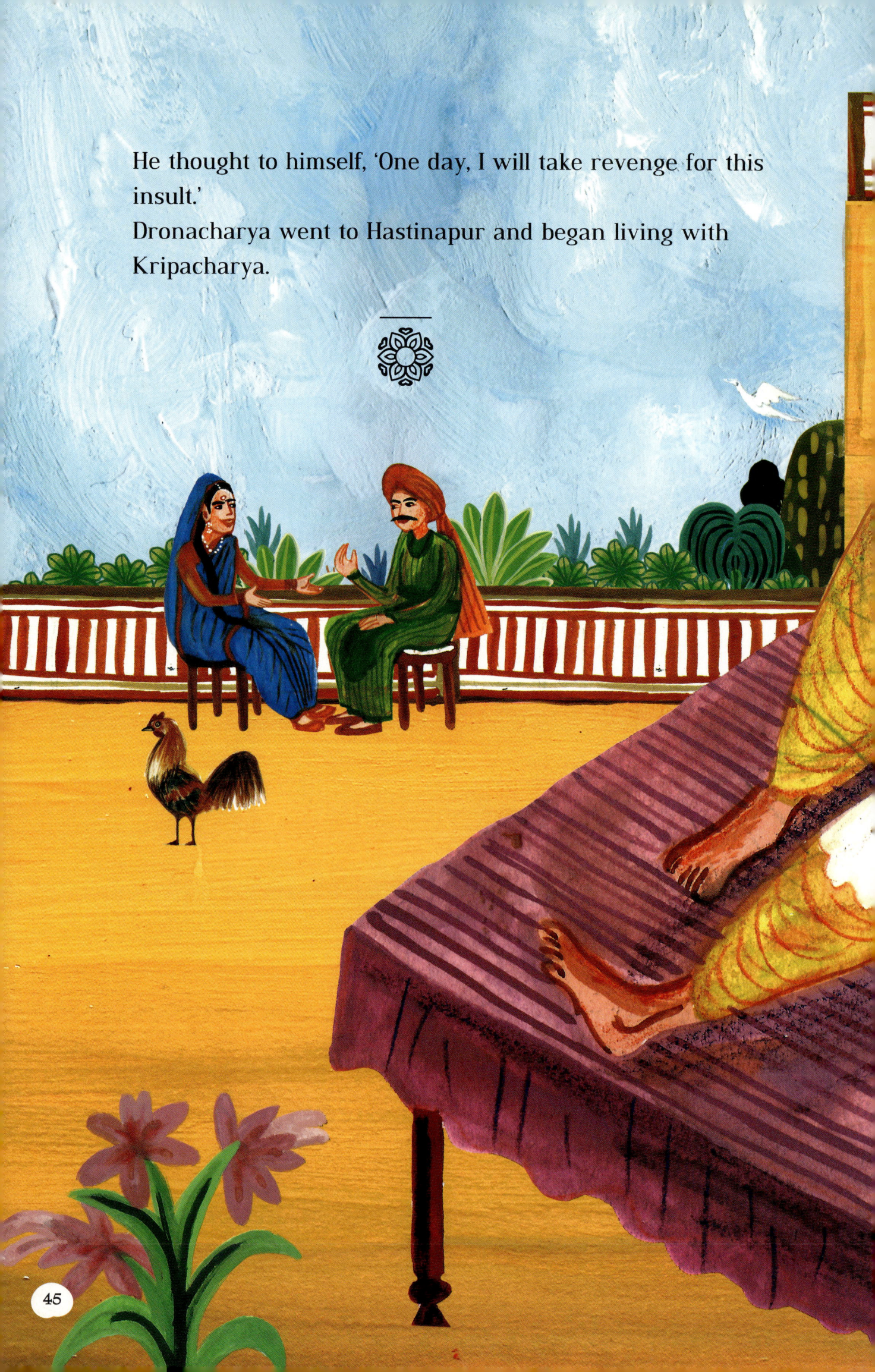

DRONACHARYA IN HASTINAPUR

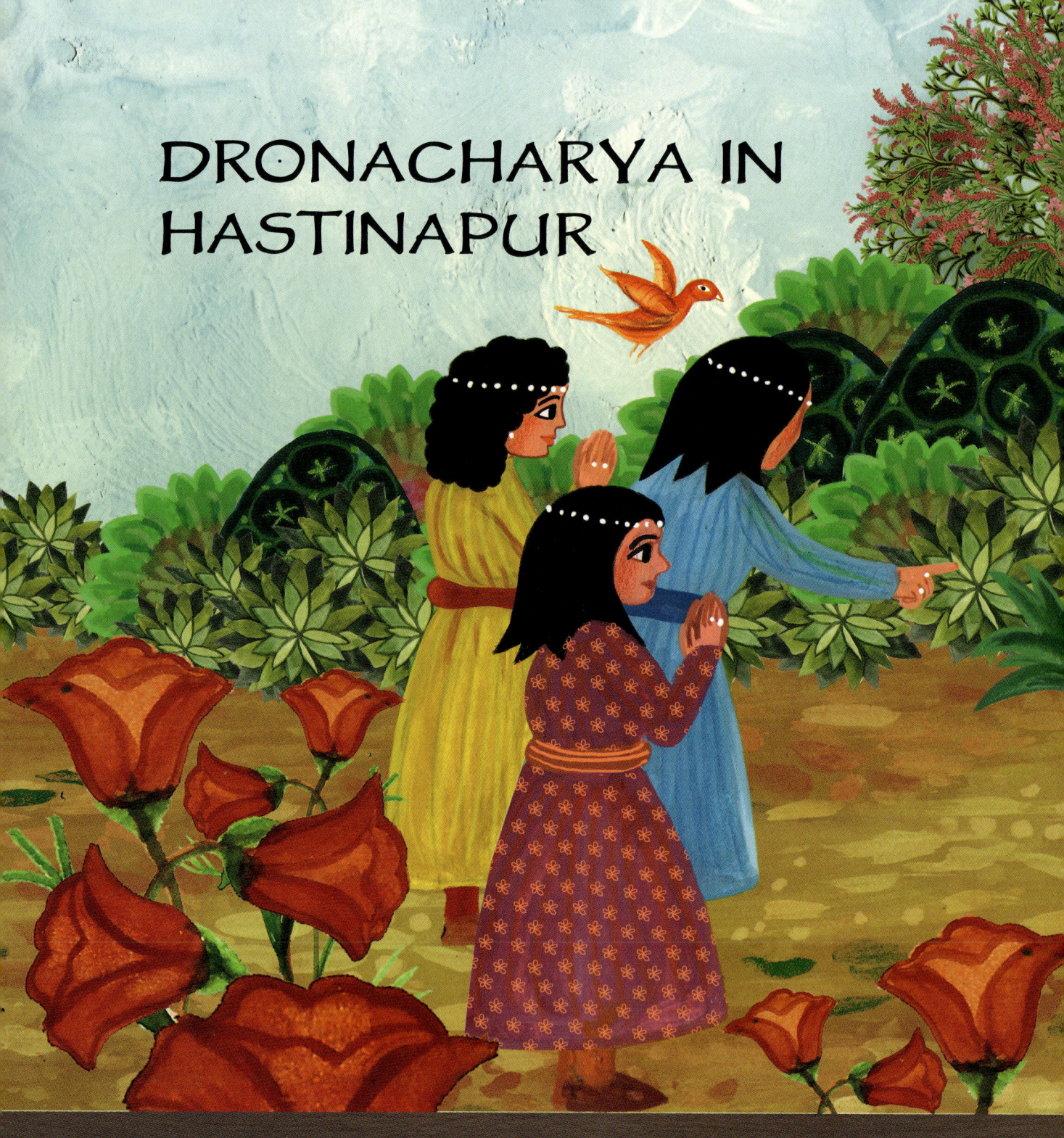

Every evening, the Kauravas and Pandavas played together in the green gardens of the palace. One day when the princes were playing, Bhima hit the ball and it fell in a nearby well. The princes rushed to the well and looked down. The ball was too far for them to reach. They stood and wondered what to do.

They saw a man sitting under a tree. It was Dronacharya. The princes went up to him and requested politely, 'Our ball has fallen into that well. Could you please help us get it back?'

Dronacharya went to the well. He took off a ring from his finger and threw it in. The princes looked at Dronacharya, confused. He smiled and said, 'Don't worry.'

Dronacharya used his bow and arrow to pull out the ring and the ball. The princes were amazed at Dronacharya's skills!

They ran back to the palace and told their grandfather Bhishma about Dronacharya's feat. Bhishma was surprised too. He sent out a messenger to call Dronacharya to his court.

Dhrithrashtra asked Dronacharya to teach his archery skills to the princes.

From that day, Dronacharya began training the princes. They learned archery and warrior skills from Dronacharya with great devotion. They practised sincerely everyday and obeyed everything their guru said.

As time passed, they grew up to be skilled warriors.

Duryodhana and Yudhishthira both dreamt of ruling Hastinapur one day.

TITLES IN THIS SERIES

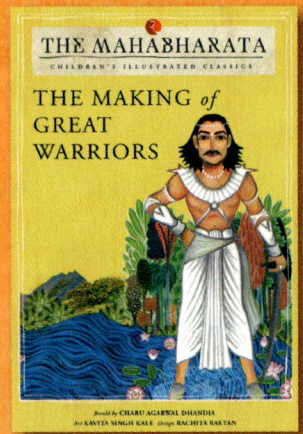
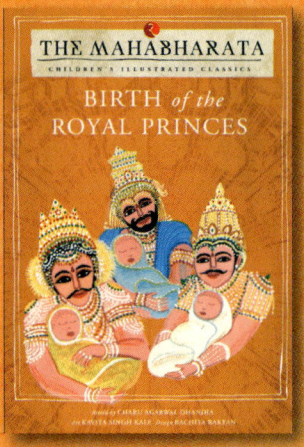
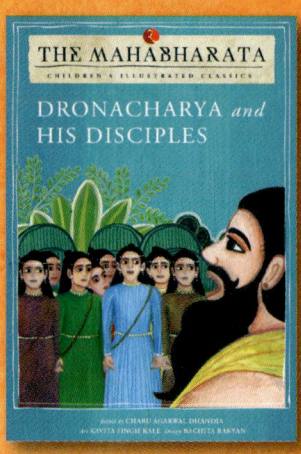
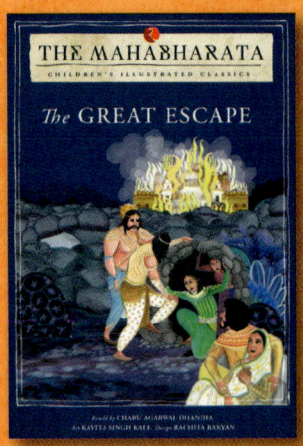
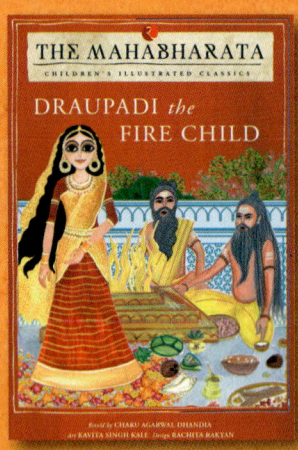
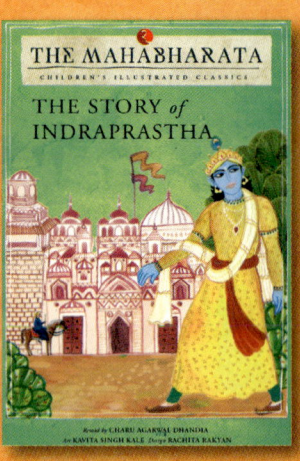
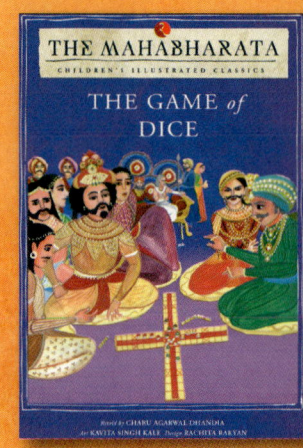
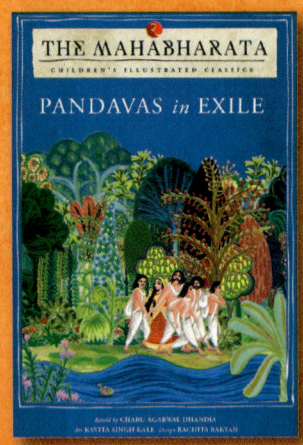
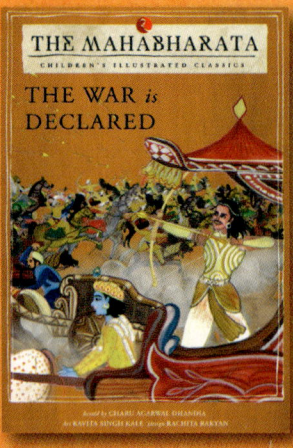